For Collin, Ila, and Kate.

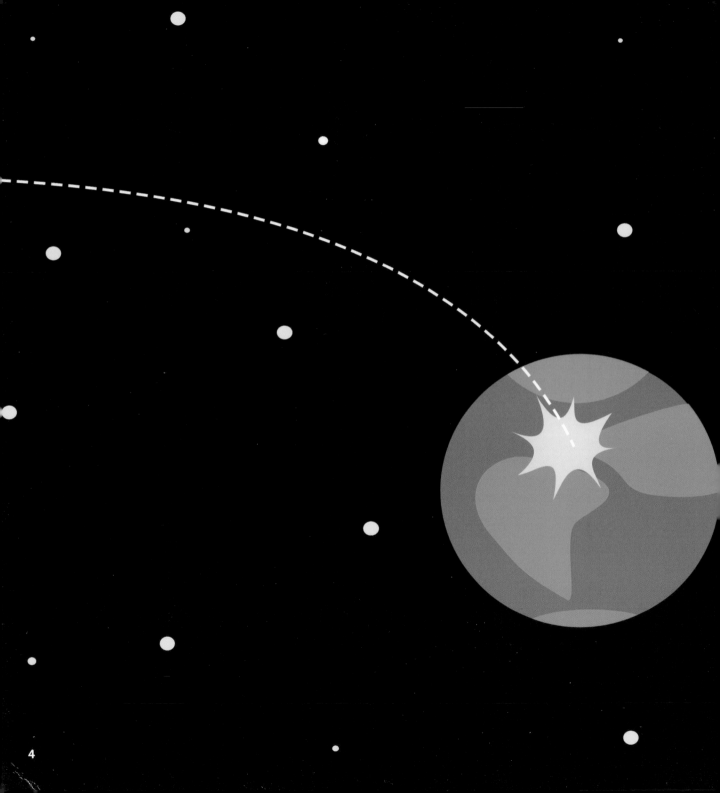

Once, something that
might seem impossible
really happened.

God—who made
stars and planets

and mountains
and trees

and you—became a baby.

He was still God, but he was also a real baby who cried and made messes and had to learn to crawl and walk. This was not what anyone expected.

People knew he
was coming. Some
expected a king.

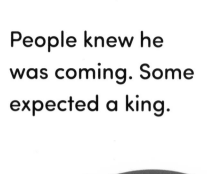

Some expected a warrior.

But most didn't think
about it at all.

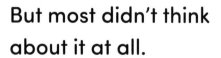

No one expected God to show up as a baby.
They had to be told.

First, Mary found out. An angel visited her on an ordinary day. He told her that God was coming as a baby and that he had picked her to be his mother.

Mary was scared. She was confused. But she said, "Okay."

Next, Joseph found out. Mary learned she was going to have the baby before she married Joseph. This caused lots of problems. Joseph was upset. He was confused. But the angel came to Joseph in his dreams and explained that this baby was God.

And he told Joseph the baby's name: Jesus, which means, "God Saves." When Joseph woke up, he thought about what the angel had told him. Then he said, *"Okay."*

Mary and Joseph said "*okay*" together. They got married and shared the strange knowledge of what was happening inside Mary. While they were getting used to their new life, Mary and Joseph found out they had to go on a long trip to a town called Bethlehem.

Jesus was born far from home. He had few friends or family nearby. Nobody but his parents knew that God had just been born.

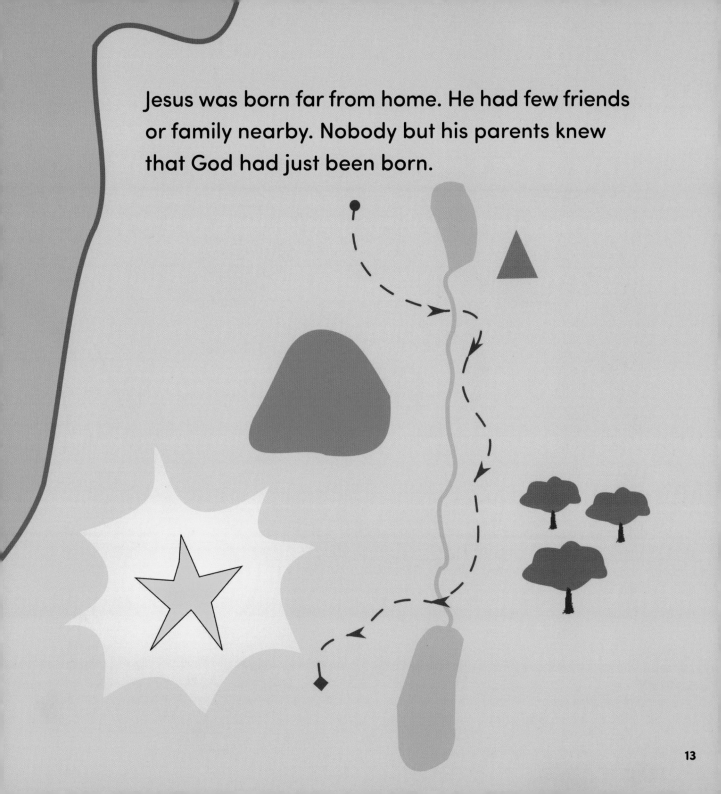

The next people to find out about Jesus were some poor shepherds. They were alone in the dark, keeping their sheep safe from robbers and wild animals overnight. Suddenly, an angel was standing there with them, shining glory like light. It was so amazing and so scary.

The angel said, "Don't worry, I have good news." And he told them what had just happened, that just over the hill in Bethlehem, God had been born as a baby.

That news was so special and good that immediately the sky was filled with angels all singing and laughing and celebrating, and the shepherds saw it all.

When it was over and the shepherds were alone again, their eyes still flashing with heavenly lights and their ears ringing with angel voices, they looked at each other and said, *"Let's go!"*

They scrambled through
the dark to town and, sure
enough, they found the baby
just like the angels had said.
They couldn't keep the news
inside. They told everybody
who would listen about the
impossible thing that had
happened that night.

Far, far away, more people were finding out that God had come as a baby. They were men who knew a lot about stars and when God showed them a special star, they knew it would lead them to the special boy. They packed up their things and said, *"Let's go."*

The wise men journeyed
for a long time, and when
they finally made it to Jesus'
town, they asked around to
figure out where he might
be. That's when Herod
found out about Jesus.

Herod was a king, but not a good one. He cared much more about being king than about the people he ruled. When he heard about the baby who was God, who had come to save his people, Herod was terrified. If this baby grew up to be a ruler, Herod wouldn't be in charge anymore. So instead of "*Okay.*" he said, "No." Instead of "*Let's go.*" he said, "Stop this."

Herod called the wise
men to the palace and
pretended to care about
the baby who was God. He
lied and said he wanted
to worship Jesus too. But
really, he was planning
something terrible.
He thought he could
make Jesus go away.

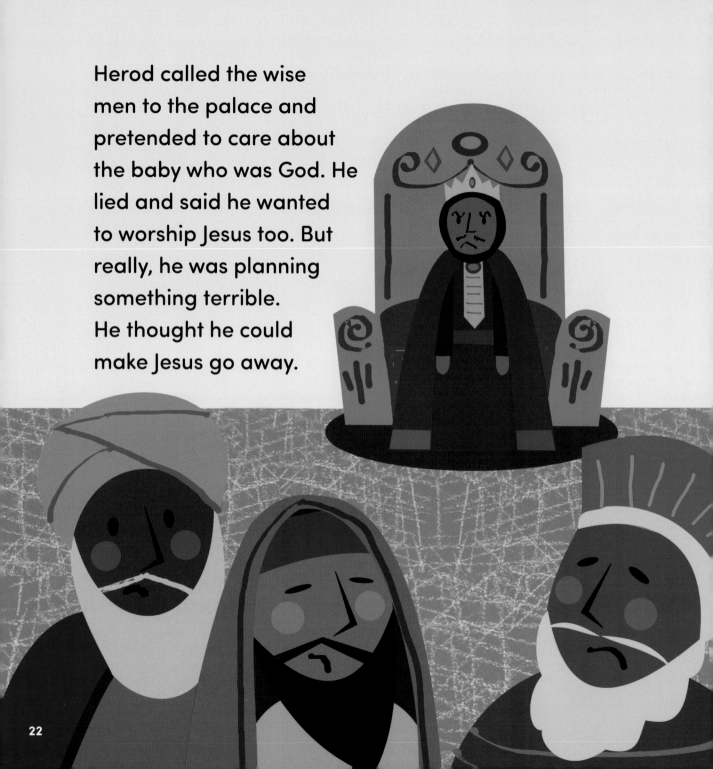

The wise men finally found Jesus. He looked just like a little boy, but they knew he was also God and they tried to make room for both of those things in their minds and hearts.

The men gave Jesus the special presents they had brought—presents that were not very fun for a little boy, but showed what a special little boy he was. Perfectly ordinary and also wholly perfect.

That night, all of the wise men had the same dream: God warned them not to go back to Herod. When they woke up, they said "Let's go," and they left without telling Herod where Jesus was.

God kept Jesus safe and he grew from a baby into a boy and then into a man—a regular man, who was also God. Every time God taught him something, he said, *"Okay."* Every time God told him to do something, he said, *"Let's go."*

Even when it was hard, even when it was scary, Jesus never said "No" to God. When the time came for him to die for the whole world, he still said, *"Okay. Let's go."* And then God did something else really unexpected. He didn't let Jesus stay dead; he brought him back to life.

Everyone who finds out about Jesus—that he is God, that he lives, that he saves us—chooses what to say to him. No matter how many times they've said "No" to God before, people who say "Okay" to Jesus get to start over and live every day with him. Knowing him and feeling his love changes everything.

This is all possible because of an unexpected gift: though God is huge and strong, he showed up as a tiny, helpless baby. God surprised us by becoming like us so that we can know him.

How to use the Unexpected Gift books

Unexpected Gift is made up of a storybook and an activity book. Each can be used separately, though they work best together and fully integrate with each other. There are 25 pages in the storybook, 25 activities in the activity book, and 25 ornaments to create.

The Storybook

The storybook tells about the Incarnation and how each of the main characters responds to it. Because it has 25 pages that correspond with the projects in the activity book, you can read the storybook all at once or a day at a time. Or both!

The Activity Book

As we learn in the storybook, the Christmas story is all about the Incarnation—God coming into the real, physical world and becoming part of it. That's why the activity book is just as important as the storybook: it makes the observation of Advent (waiting for the celebration of Christmas) hands-on and tangible. Making an actual thing every day will help you reflect on how God made himself a physical being for us. Each project corresponds with the storybook page and ornament for that day.

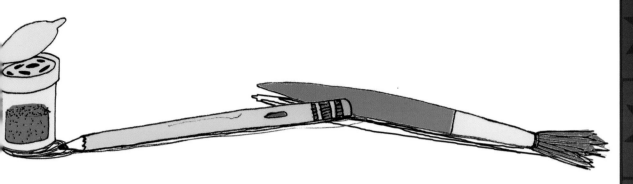

The Ornaments

Also found in the activity book, each ornament has one verse that links to both the storybook and the craft for the day. Day by day, as you add them together, you will end up with a telling of the nativity story through Scripture. You can hang the ornaments on a real or paper Christmas tree, on a string to make a garland, on your refrigerator, or your window! Whatever works for you. We just recommend hanging them where you can see them. You're adorning your home with truth and it will be good to be reminded throughout the Advent season.

Further Discussion

 Kids have some great questions about Christmas—sometimes pretty tough questions. You can download a further discussion guide with some answers to FAQs by scanning the QR code.

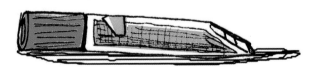

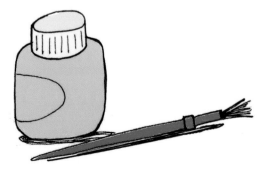

Unexpected Gift